wn I   Knight   Bishop   Queen   King   Warder   Pawn II

wn I   Knight   Bishop   Queen   King   Warder   Pawn II

wn I   Knight   Bishop   Queen   King   Warder   Pawn II

wn I   Knight   Bishop   Queen   King   Warder   Pawn II

THE LEWIS CHESSMEN

and what happened to them

It seemed to most of the chessmen that they had always been there...

THE LEWIS CHESSMEN

and what happened to them

by

Irving Finkel

Illustrated by

Clive Hodgson

British Museum Press

To

Humfry, Jemima, Harry,

George and Dorothy

———◆———

Published by British Museum Press
A division of British Museum Publications,
46 Bloomsbury Street, London WC1B 3QQ

A catalogue record for this book is available from the British Library

ISBN 0 7141 0573 2

Cover design by James Shurmer
Edited by Carolyn Jones
Printed in Great Britain by Henry Ling, Dorset

Replicas of the Lewis Chessmen are available from the British Museum Gift Shop
or by mail order. Please ring 0171 323 1234 for a free catalogue.

CONTENTS

Isle of Lewis

Uig

Edinburgh

British Museum
London

BACKGROUND TO THE STORY

For many years the walrus-ivory chessmen from the Isle of Lewis in the Outer Hebrides have been divided between the British Museum in London and the Royal Museum of Scotland in Edinburgh. They have delighted generations of visitors with their wonderful detailed carving, their solid, dependable shapes, and their unexpectedly expressive faces.

The hoard of at least seventy-eight pieces was found with some ivory draughtsmen and a belt buckle. Originally some were stained red, but nowadays all trace of the colour has been lost. Many archaeologists believe that the chessmen were manufactured in Scandinavia, perhaps in Norway, and for various reasons they have dated the pieces to around 1150 AD.

What remains altogether unknown is how the chessmen came to be on the Isle of Lewis. It has been suggested that they might have been the stock-in-trade of a travelling ivory merchant. They were discovered somewhere on a beach on the north side of the island in 1831. Exact details concerning the find have been lost, although there are several differing traditions on record.

A Captain Roderick Ririe from Stornaway sold the chessmen for £30 in the spring of 1831 to Mr T.A. Forrest, an Edinburgh dealer in curiosities. The chessmen were subsequently separated. Sixty-seven were purchased for £84 in November 1831 from Mr Forrest by the Trustees of the British Museum. However, ten chessmen had earlier been acquired by the collector Mr Charles Kirkpatrick Sharpe, who also managed to secure one further piece, a bishop, directly from Lewis. These eleven pieces were later bought by Lord Londesborough, and eventually acquired in 1888 for the Royal Museum of Scotland.

This book follows the story, as far as we can know it, of the adventures experienced by the Lewis Chessmen after they came to light in the nineteenth century. It ends with the Big Surprise that befell them in September 1993, when they were all temporarily reunited, for the first time since 1831, at a Special Exhibition of Chessmen at the British Museum in London.

For further details concerning the history of the pieces, see Michael Taylor, *The Lewis Chessmen* (British Museum Press, 1978, reprinted 1995)

Part I

CHAPTER I

In Which the Chessmen Languish Underground

It was always Dark inside the Chamber, of course. The temperature was usually reasonably comfortable, and the older pieces could sometimes feel in their bones when Spring turned to Summer, or Autumn to Winter, but the Darkness itself was unchanging.

Everybody was used to it, though. And things were fairly acceptable otherwise. The place was roomy enough, with an elegantly high ceiling. It was sometimes a bit dampish at one end, so most of them avoided that

part, except those with thirsty horses to worry about. And it was Home.

It seemed to most of the chessmen that they had always been there. This was one of the Periodic Topics of Discussion that often cropped up in the evenings. Some of the lesser royalty had a decided leaning towards philosophical speculation, and the question of whether they had always been there would often lead to the more difficult 'Why Are We Here?' and 'What Will Happen to Us?'

The Bishops always regarded this sort of thinking as dangerous. They naturally saw things in terms of Divine Plans, and recommended Uncomplaining Acceptance of their situation.

The Knights and Warders took a wholly different view. They kept up their spirits with manly talk among themselves of battles, of fabulous battles remembered in the old stories and wonderful battles to come. The Kings didn't discourage that at all. For one thing it prevented dissatisfaction, and anyway one or two rather fancied seeing a bit of heroic rescuing or sword-play themselves.

There was one cranky and ponderous older King, a little bowed now and never seen to wear a beard, who claimed that he could remember a time *before* they were in the Chamber. His reminiscences were always greeted with incredulity by the younger ones, but occasionally someone could persuade him to speak of the Boat, and Endless Seasickness. Sometimes he said that, in a bad dream, he could feel the rushing wind, the violence and the panic, and the stabbing breath of the man running along the beach before the great crash. Truth to tell many of the other older pieces had a fitful memory of such things too, but most were reluctant to think about them, and they would never speak a word about the matter themselves.

The chessmen were buried fairly deeply. Their voices sometimes echoed in the Chamber, but they couldn't identify for certain any of the faint noises that came from outside.

One February there were unusually high seas. Day after day the heavy rollers crashed onto the beach, dragging at the sands, undermining the tough grasses that struggled defiantly in the wintry air. The chessmen shivered, and huddled closer together. None could anticipate it, but they were on the verge of an Adventure...

CHAPTER 2

In Which the Cow makes a Break-through

Everything, of a sudden, began to change. One morning there was an excited flurry because, beyond argument, something was happening. The air was colder, and from a distance new noises could be made out. One, they decided, must be the Sea itself.

The Queens were instantly all of a flutter. One or two, swept up in the general feeling of exhilaration, decided to rebraid their hair. This was a lengthy job which most of them rather tended to pass up as a rule, since they had to do their husbands' locks as well as their own, and it was fiddly work with cold fingers. But the unwonted draughts of fresh, salty air that swept through the Chamber affected everybody. Knights and Warders could be detected sprucing up their tunics. Rather cobwebby swords were brushed off and polished, and even the ponies were treated to some military grooming after a lamentable period of neglect.

So when the Cow finally put in its appearance, they all happened to be looking their best.

They often argued afterwards about what really happened. Many were busy talking, dozing or otherwise preoccupied at the actual moment. The most reliable testimony probably comes from the Knights, who were experienced lookouts. They agree with what the calmer Warders say they can remember.

All are positive that it was really a cow. There was a cataclysmic upheaval, the Chamber was filled with blinding sunlight and freezing

air, and the huge, dripping mouth of the Cow suddenly swung into view. It was steadily chewing grasses, its eyes rolling in surprise and foolish curiosity as it peered into the hole. A hoof was planted ominously close. The chessmen reared back, the Queens pallid and fainting, the Kings stolid beside them, ready to draw their swords and apparently unruffled. The Knights and Warders sprang into formation, fanning out around the yellowing thrones, blocking any access and poised, just as they had practised, for Battle.

Their steady gaze unnerved the Cow. It backed off, still chewing, to look for more conventional fodder. The royalty relaxed slightly, and many held hands. For the first time since most of them could remember, they could see one another clearly. Time had taken its toll. Many Kings were grizzled, and years of contemplation without much exercise had left them perhaps portlier than their wives remembered. The Queens,

on the other hand, seemed somehow more careworn and anxious, and one or two, gazing at the pale faces of the others, thought with a pang about rouge, and mirrors.

But there was no time for much daydreaming of this kind. Another peril was approaching. A heavy tread along the shingle could be heard, and then suddenly the grasses parted again and another huge face loomed into view. This face was human, red, rough and unshaven. Like the Cow, the Man rolled his eyes, and startled everybody with a sudden cry. There was a crash as he dropped his spade, and he ran off as

fast as possible. The chessmen were alone again, out in the world, con-
fused and unprotected. They looked at one another in silence. Hearts
were beating fast, but they were ready for anything.

CHAPTER 3

In Which the Chessmen Encounter Human Greed and Avarice

I t was turning dark. As it grew chillier the chessmen became apprehensive. The Kings worried about the damage, and discussed possible repairs with the Warders. They were deep in technical conversation when suddenly everybody froze. There were more footsteps, and two low voices, one fearful and reluctant, the other defiant and rather bullying. A pair of giant silhouettes loomed against the night sky. One was the Man from the morning, the other, burly beside him, his Wife.

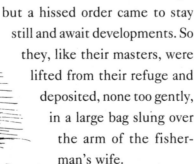

'Go on with you, you fool ...'

'... they're elves, little devils I tell you ...'

'... nothing of the kind, they're not moving. We'll sell them ...'

'... *You* pick them up then.'

Large, calloused hands, by no means fastidiously clean, lurched closer, and began to pick up the chessmen one by one, turning them over in the fading light. The Warders at the front bristled and swore revenge,

but a hissed order came to stay still and await developments. So they, like their masters, were lifted from their refuge and deposited, none too gently, in a large bag slung over the arm of the fisherman's wife.

The Bag itself, they later remembered, was

one of the worst parts of the Adventure. For one thing, it was clear that its usual job was to transport seaweed, or herring. It was far from suitable as a carriage for ivory-complexioned monarchs grown unaccustomed to much in the way of drama. Those at the bottom suffered the worst, since the bouncing stride of the fisherman's wife had the bag swinging in a vigorous arc as she made her way back to the cottage. Many of the chessmen, higgledy-piggledy in the lower recesses, wished heartily that they were safely back underground again.

Eventually it was clear that they had reached a cottage. Cool night air was promptly replaced by a muggy interior heavy with peat smoke. The bag was thumped down on a hard surface. From what the chessmen could make out through the cloth, the Man and his wife doused the lamps and went noisily and wheezily to bed. The chessmen made themselves as comfortable as they could for the night, and eventually went to sleep too.

CHAPTER 4

In Which the Chessmen pass into Commercial Hands

'I'll give you ten pounds the lot, and you're well rid of such pagan things ...' There was a muffled reply, and Captain Ririe grunted impatiently.

The bag swung violently from side to side. There followed whole days like that, with mysterious movements that propelled the chessmen from place to place, and from land to sea and back again. Heroic Warders took spells of duty in the dangerous area by the neck of the bag, where it was easier to hear what was going on outside, and reported back half-heard conversations when they could.

It became simpler after a while to stay asleep. They were used to long periods of hibernation when nothing much was afoot, so many of the pieces gave themselves up to semi-slumber. The Kings put their arms around their Queens, knowing that their brave retainers would give them the best of protection if necessary.

Some time later, when they were still only half-awake, the bag was suddenly slit open, and the chessmen found themselves gently tumbled out into the light again. This time they landed on a large, crowded desk. They spilled out, giddy and untidy, onto the smooth wood, and found themselves being scrutinised under a lamp. This Man's eye was penetrating, and the Queens felt themselves much disadvantaged at first, but his fingers were gentle, and gradually the chessmen relaxed. It seemed that they were safe from violence at least.

17

With an instinctive deference the Man began to set out the chess-men, Kings and Queens together, with the other pieces separated off at a respectful distance. There were many other things piled about on the desk and elsewhere in the room. A brass microscope gleamed under the lamp, and there were further objects that none of the chess-men, with their rather old-fashioned perspective, could identify. There was even a set of what they realised with a shock must be meant to be chessmen, untutored and crude *sticks* of varnished *boxwood*. They all looked instantly away lest the earthy-looking knights should attempt any familiarity. These most humble chessmen, however, luxuriated smugly on a real wooden chess-board, at which all the Lewis pieces gazed with secret longing. It was many a year since they had stood ranged on a chess-board, each in his or her proper place, with one job to do in a fixed universe, and no unexpected international travel.

After a long silence the man spoke suddenly in the quiet room. 'Well, well, the best bargain I ever made.'

CHAPTER 5

In Which the Chessmen know the Bitterness of Parting

For some time now life went on peacefully. Every day their new guardian would come over and peer fixedly at them, admiring individuals in turn, muttering to himself as he posed them this way and that. This sort of adulation irritated the Kings, and went unnoticed by the lower ranks, but it did wonders for some of the Queens, for whom male appreciation tended to come but rarely nowadays. For some reason the Man couldn't perceive for himself who was married to whom, and he often separated couples who would have preferred to be securely within reach of one another. Still, when it came to nightfall they were all safely stowed away well clear of the edge of the table, and nobody felt really resentful.

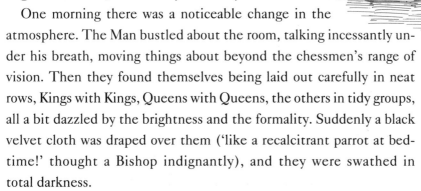

One morning there was a noticeable change in the atmosphere. The Man bustled about the room, talking incessantly under his breath, moving things about beyond the chessmen's range of vision. Then they found themselves being laid out carefully in neat rows, Kings with Kings, Queens with Queens, the others in tidy groups, all a bit dazzled by the brightness and the formality. Suddenly a black velvet cloth was draped over them ('like a recalcitrant parrot at bedtime!' thought a Bishop indignantly), and they were swathed in total darkness.

The cloth by and large muffled sounds, but they could distinguish that there were now two contrasting voices in conversation moving round the room. They were all tense suddenly: misgivings swept through them all. Slowly the cloth was pulled away again.

'... Perhaps you'd like to take a look at these, Mr Sharpe ...

... You'll never see anything like them again ...

... Thought of you as soon as I got hold of them ...

... Real connoisseur's choice ...

... gentleman's cabinet ...'

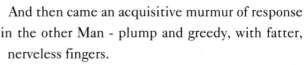

And then came an acquisitive murmur of response in the other Man - plump and greedy, with fatter, nerveless fingers.

'I only managed to get seventy-seven of them in the end. The man who found them was a superstitious imbecile, and I imagine that he probably dropped some. Then there were two or three grubby people in between. One of them went back to the findspot to see if any were there still, but apparently there were not. I haven't been able to get over there myself, what with the weather and business. So we have most of four sets here, plus a few extra pieces. Rather a shortage in pawns I'm afraid, if you're thinking of actually playing with them. But what workmanship ... Have you seen the carving on the chairs?'

'*Chairs*!' thought the Kings and Queens (and a few of the Bishops) in disgust.

'It's going to have to be two guineas each right across the board, I'm afraid. At seventy-seven pieces that comes out at one hundred and fifty-four guineas all told, but I could let them go for one hundred and fifty, since you are something of a special customer.'

The other whistled softly, and murmured something about 'the possibility, Mr Forrest, of splitting them up'. The two men stepped over to the window, their backs turned to the chessmen.

The leading pieces exchanged worried looks. They had always known that they would be sold one day, of course, that was what they had been made for, but somehow not like this. In any case they had been together for so long now that the group felt more natural as it was. It was many centuries since the wizened old carver in the Far North had lined them up on the bench and decided who would marry whom, and who would look after whom, testing them on his huge old chess-board, searching for the best arrangements.

'Well, it goes against the grain, but since none of the sets is complete I could contemplate selling a small group to you separately first,

if you couldn't think of taking the whole collection. I thought that they would be interested at the Antiquaries' Society, but to tell the truth it is always a slow business with the museums anyway. I could see my way to letting *you* have a dozen or so, if you could settle with me directly. Would you care for any of the red pieces? I think they are particularly pretty myself, and there aren't so many of them.'

The second man lingered very consid- erably over his choice. The chessmen were agonised. Helpless and vulnerable they awaited their fate. Would he recognise who belonged with whom, and take what he could of the same family, or would he blunder hopelessly and most cruelly divide them? All held their breath, fearing the worst.

'They seem to come in different sizes, do they not?' enquired the Collector.

'Indeed,' returned the other, 'but you cannot make up proper sets. I've tried these many evenings without success. Take what you prefer.'

In the end Mr Sharpe put aside one greater King, two greater Queens, a lesser King and Queen (who *were* married), two greater Bishops and one lesser Bishop, with just a single Knight and a Warder of each size to look after them. What a hodge-podge! What folly!

The chessmen burned with indignation and frustration. *They* knew how they were meant to be and where they were sup- posed to stand, and here were these inept and myopic merchants dividing husbands from wives, and interfering left right and centre with the natu- ral order of things, and all for mere money.

Notwithstanding their pleading stares, the Dealer relinquished the selection to the Col- lector. He removed several silk handkerchiefs from various pockets, and began to wrap each piece carefully and individually. The two Queens and the King who were to be left behind gazed speechlessly as their partners disappeared into the col- ourful bands of material and were buried in the copious pockets about the Collector's person. To crown their discomfiture they then witnessed gold passing from hand to hand. The Collector left, promising that if he could raise more capital he would return before long for more of the treasure. The Dealer closed the door behind him with a complacent sigh, and went to stow the coins in his strong box.

For the first time in about six hundred and fifty years the chessmen were parted.

CHAPTER 6

In Which Philosophy is Seriously Tested

After this traumatic afternoon the chessmen were glad to be placed in a box and left alone. Their wounds were deep and painful, and those most powerfully affected preferred to lie in solitude and reflect. It was, of course, to be expected that a professional chess-piece might have his nearest and dearest suddenly taken from him in the Great Game. Indeed, this was a matter that Kings were trained to accept from birth, but there was a feeling of permanence about this separation that made it a real disaster, both socially and personally.

Part II

CHAPTER 7

In Which Great Men Intervene for the Benefit of the Nation

'I understand, Gentlemen,' said the Chairman of the Trustees in the British Museum very deliberately, 'that these - *ahem* - ivory chessmen are indeed truly remarkable, and Mr Madden kindly informs me in his written account (which I have before me) that we should accord the offer to - *ahem* - acquire them our ..."very sympathetic consideration." They have been exhibited, albeit briefly, in Edinburgh, and Mr Madden is anxious that we should act swiftly lest the competition steal a march on us. You will recall that this same group came up for offer recently at a sum we considered at the time (after due reflection) to be excessive. The sum named at that juncture was (if I might just check in my papers) some One Hundred Guineas. Well, Mr Madden has tirelessly pursued his quest, and persuaded (or should I say bludgeoned?) the present owner into viewing with favour a possible offer of Eighty-

Four pounds instead. This investment would procure for the Museum a total of - *ahem* - sixty-seven chess pieces (more than one really needs to play the game, surely?) together with fourteen draughtsmen, and a single ivory belt-buckle. Mr Madden points out (perhaps a little wildly?) that these pieces of carving are calculated to appeal to the General Public, and that they would undoubtedly constitute (*if* we should view this as a desirable quality) an attraction to them. He even goes so far as to intimate that they might be - *ahem* - popular ...'

———◆———

Mr Madden took snuff, and he took plenty in his excitement at finally unwrapping the chessmen in his room after their long and rocky coach-ride from Edinburgh. As a result of their recent escapades the chessmen had become resigned to facing an unpredictable and unsettled future, but the Dealer had wrapped them up with such care that they felt destined to end up in appreciative hands. Most of them had slept deeply throughout the journey.

The room in which they now emerged was striking. The walls were lined with large books in glass-fronted wooden bookcases. There was a greater confusion of miscellaneous objects than they had ever seen at once before, exceeding that in the old carver's workshop, and even greater than that in the Dealer's house. The pieces found themselves once again standing on a desk under a bright light, but here they felt much more at home. Once again a human face was peering down at them, but the owner of the face was humming ecstatically, and he was smiling contentedly as each new piece emerged from the straw and joined its fellows among the books and pots on the leather-topped desk.

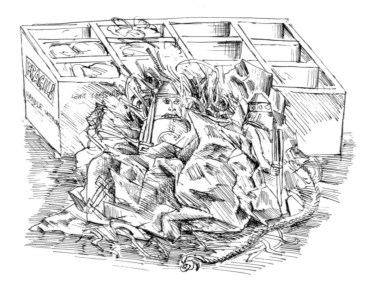

Finally, they were all free. The curator (for it was Mr Madden) sighed deeply, and leaned back in his chair. 'Welcome to the British Museum,' he whispered.

CHAPTER 8

In Which Acquisitiveness Reaps its Due Reward

In Scotland, the Collector was dead. He had succumbed peacefully after a rather excessive lunch while dozing over a portfolio of newly-acquired engravings. The chessmen noticed the case slip from his hands and slide over his belly, but they thought that he was asleep (as was often the case after meals). It was only when the housemaid shrieked later that afternoon that they realised what had happened.

The three Bishops made appropriate gestures and pious remarks among themselves, but studiously avoided eye-contact with the monarchs, who still loathed and resented the Collector and the consequences of his selfish cupidity. They all watched steadily through the glass as the doctor came and pronounced him officially dead, and over the next few days they followed with fascination the preparations, the receptions, and the general hypocrisy of mercenary people's conversation.

A respectable number of weeks elapsed after the funeral. One afternoon a thin young man, the Secretary to a Lord, came to the house. He was shown into the Study, where everything of the Collector's had been left untouched.

The young man looked swiftly around the room, and then came to stand in front of the glass cabinet. He peered carefully through the glass, polishing the pane with his neckerchief where his eager breath had misted it up. 'Ah, there you are,' he remarked, counting with a bony fingertip.

The Collector's widow was entirely black in her dress, pink of cheek, and damp of eye. Briskly the young man intimated that these (he pointed accordingly) were the ten ivory pieces in question, that it was these (he pointed again) in which his Lordship was interested for his Own Collection, and that it was these for which he had been instructed to make his Lordship's offer together with expressions of condolence to the grieving widow. The Secretary had, of course, arrived armed with the appropriate sum in gold coins. The room was gloomy with the sombre drapes across the windows, and the chessmen had to strain to see what was taking place.

'...we got one more from the Island years ago,' she was saying, 'I think it was one of the bishops ...' The Secretary coughed delicately. 'Mr Sharpe's express wish was that everything should go through the Auction Rooms,' she continued, eyeing the money, ' to give the other collectors a chance. It's all in the will, and I've told the same to all of them.'

The Secretary swept the shiny coins deftly back into their velvet bag, clinking them slightly as he did so. He winked discreetly at the Queens through the glass, bowed respectfully to all the pieces, and whispered, 'Leave this to me.'

———◆———

After the Auction the Secretary was full of smiles. He unlocked the cabinet, and with light and skilful fingers he removed the chessmen one by one (winking at the Queens as he did so) and packed them carefully into a polished, impressively monogrammed briefcase.

29

As the Widow dragged a meditative finger in the faint dust revealed on the shelf by the chessmen's departure, the Secretary was already closing the front door behind him. Thereafter he was conveyed with considerable speed and accuracy by the Coachman to his Lordship's own residence, secure in the back of his Lordship's own carriage.

'Utterly splendid work, my boy,' said Lord Londesborough later that afternoon. 'I have pined after those chess-pieces for years, but he would never relinquish them. Now, where shall we put them, do you think?'

CHAPTER 9

In Which Modesty and Self-Restraint are Seriously Tested

'Dear Mr ...,' wrote Mr Madden, 'it having seemed to me that the Members of this Society would welcome ...' He lowered his pen, and looked again at the glowing ivory chessmen on parade about his desk as usual. He had for some time been engaged on a compendious history of the Game of Chess, but the arrival of *his* (as he saw them) Isle of Lewis chessmen had affected him deeply, and it seemed fitting to inform the world about them without delay. When he was safely alone with them in his room he was apt to address them directly, and had been doing so for so long that a reply from one or another would not have astonished him at all. 'I'm going to make you famous,' he confided. 'We'll have a proper paper for the Antiquaries, likenesses and all, and everyone will appreciate you at last.'

The chessmen had no objection to being handled by Mr Madden. He looked at them with an informed and sympathetic eye, and had the endearing habit of noticing something that intrigued him about all of them and writing it down carefully on his paper. This was almost as pleasing as his gentle measurements, not just from top to bottom, but in other directions as well. His careful use of the tape-measure led one or two of the Warders to conclude that he planned to provide them with new uniforms, especially when they saw how carefully he sketched their helmets and other paraphernalia. Each of the sixty-seven pieces was treated to this gratifying ritual, and Mr Madden worked long and patient hours in the winter evenings by his sputtering gas lamp.

He *had* wanted, he explained to them after a month or two, to have a drawing of each and every one of them in his report, but alas that was not going to be possible. The expense was prohibitive, because each Portrait would have to be engraved for the printer, and that would cost more money than the Society would release. 'They've let me do one of each of you, and that's all.'

He suffered truly in the uncomfortable position of having to choose. Since all the pieces were fond of him they tried to act like adults when he finally made his selection for the artist. After he went home that evening, however, there were some very unseemly squabbles and exhibitions of pettiness on the part of certain pieces who pined after a modelling career and were uncontrollably jealous and hurt by their rejection.

CHAPTER 10

In Which Literary Endeavour is shown to Have its Drawbacks

Light-heartedly Mr Madden slid the great wad of papers into a stiff envelope, and folded over the end securely. His scratchy pen squeaked out the correct name and address in elegant copperplate, and with a theatrical flourish he sealed the envelope with his signet, and rang the bell imperiously for the Messenger. 'It is finished, Ladies and Gentlemen,' he said, and bowed low in the direction of the assembled chessmen. 'It's off to the printer with the papers and we now have the pleasant task of passively awaiting our proofs.' The Messenger came in just as he was helping himself to a rewarding pinch of snuff, and the envelope over which he had toiled so long but with such pleasure disappeared into a large bag.

An unforeseen but painful consequence to this literary achievement was that Mr Madden no longer had an excuse to keep the Lewis Chessmen in his room. He remembered rather belatedly how he had stressed their Universal Appeal to the Trustees as a strong argument in favour of buying them, and so the point had come when perhaps he had better do something about showing them to the Public. He sighed ruefully, and rang the bell again to summon one of his long-serving assistants ...

The chessmen felt far from secure in the trembling hands of Mr Madden's Assistant. A special case was ready for them, lined with velvet, and certainly very comfortable-looking, but they were completely unprepared for the horrible feeling of nakedness that came upon them when they were actually placed, wobbling a trifle, in their new home. All four sides of the case were of glass, and thus they had no privacy whatever. With sinking hearts the chessmen eyed their surroundings. They were in a large gallery, surrounded by other cages rather like their own. They could make out other objects of ivory that were vaguely familiar from a long time before. The Bishops noticed with approval some admirable reliquaries just across the way. Perhaps it wouldn't be so bad after all ...

CHAPTER 11

In Which Strictness in Upbringing is Vindicated

Much further north their eleven fellow chessmen lived side-by-side with stags' heads and burnished armour. Lesser chessmen would have suffered terribly from the damp and the draughts, but the Lewis pieces had their roots in chilly Scandinavia, and this sort of problem, which greatly troubled the human inhabitants of the Castle, did not distress them at all.

CHAPTER 12

In Which the Disadvantages of Fame become Apparent

On Visiting Days those fortunate people who managed to secure a ticket to the British Museum seemed spellbound by the chessmen, just as Mr Madden had promised they would. The Attendants were always trying to hurry people on round the galleries, and they came to dread the moment when the visitors got to the Chess Case, because no-one wanted to leave. On the contrary, they seemed to want to glue their noses to the glass, and when they were finally persuaded to move on, they were much less interested in whatever they were shown next.

This adoration did something to soothe the initial distress of the more self-conscious of the chessmen. Several of the Queens, especially the red ones, found their exposed position quite unsuited to their sensibilities. 'It's like being in a zoo, but on the wrong side of the bars,' one confided to another. For consolation they practised Grimaces and disapproving, We-Are-Not-Amused stares which they could direct back at the gaping masses.

CHAPTER 13

In Which Further Fateful Steps are Taken

'You'll recall that most of the chessmen have been in that museum in London for years,' insisted a Scottish curator, many years later, seated round a table with various long-suffering colleagues.

'I'm thinking that this auction is our opportunity to get Lord Londesborough's eleven chessmen for a Scottish Museum, and that we should act pronto ...'

CHAPTER 14

In Which Virtue is Rewarded

One morning in the British Museum, some years later, Mr Madden rapped gently with his knuckles on the case. Most of the chessmen still had their eyes closed against the early morning sunshine which streamed across the gallery. Mr Madden's eyes were excited and his movements unpredictable, since he was clutching a telegram. 'Your various Majesties, Ladies and Gentlemen,' he whispered urgently, 'Pray inspect this historic document!' He pressed the flimsy paper upside-down to the glass, and the outer flank of Knights squinted in their efforts to decipher the message. 'It is I,' he explained, 'once your plain Mr Madden, Servant to the Trustees, and now *Sir Frederic*. Our Queen has declared me a Knight too. For *Services to Chessmen*.'

This most satisfactory news was met with sober appreciation by all the assembly. 'High time too,' was the general feeling, and 'It couldn't have happened to a worthier person.'

For years Mr Madden had invariably visited the chessmen at least once a day, just to make sure that they were all right. With this new development he was in and out of the gallery more or less perpetually. He discreetly studied the Knights afresh to capture in his mind's eye their instinctive comportment, and the Queens smiled to themselves to see him practising his bow at the far end of the gallery.

As ever, the Warders provided information for the rest of the chessmen. They were strategically posted within the show-case, and even under the peaceful conditions that usually prevailed in the Museum they were on half-alert. Thus they were able to report that their larger, uniformed counterparts in the Museum also approved of Mr Madden's imminent transformation. These gallery warders (with whom they felt a measure of fellowship) sometimes patrolled together in the vicinity of the case. Whenever the topic came up in conversation, the report came back, the gallery warders felt it was a Good Thing.

Sir Frederic came later to show them his badge. He seemed noticeably taller, and evidently had new clothes and a new top hat too.

Some months after that, out of the blue, the chessmen were taken out one by one and specially dusted. There was a vigorous display by many men in overalls involving paintbrushes and pots of varnish and special rolls of carpet. There was, it transpired, to be a Royal Visit ...

Sir Frederic accompanied Her Majesty around the Antiquities, steering her entourage deftly between the monuments, and finally coming to rest before his sixty-seven chessmen. The Queen stooped slightly to peer through the freshly-polished glass. Her glance passed idly among the rank and file, lingering on the stately Kings for a moment, before coming to rest, eye to eye, with the oldest of the Queens. Her own imperious look was returned unblinkingly. Her Majesty faltered slightly, and then remarked that she didn't care for chess. The party moved on.

CHAPTER 15

In Which the Ages of Man Reveal Themselves

There was a long period after that when little enough seemed to happen. More and more people were allowed to come to the Museum, but the chessmen had become used to their strange existence, and most faced even the busiest of days with equanimity. One game they played among themselves was to see if they could recognise people through the glass from earlier visits. Sometimes London families would come often over the years, and the more observant chessmen identified particular children on the Other Side who gradually turned into adults, and ultimately became parents themselves.

CHAPTER 16

In Which Human Folly Reigns Unchecked

At one point there was a noticeable falling-off in Attendance. For weeks almost nobody came to admire them, and the chessmen noticed other changes too. None of the curators whistled, for example, and the gallery warders looked grim and depressed. Things came to a head one night when they were startled awake by an explosion. Clouds of dust swirled in the corridors, and there was broken glass and smashed pottery all about. People ran around with buckets, and someone banged anxiously on their case to see if they were unharmed.

The next morning two Boy Assistants with tense faces came to rescue them. They were swiftly taken away on a trolley, and after a quick check, a pat on the back each and a kiss for the Ladies they were wrapped in cotton wool, and packed in a big box marked DELICATE and IVORY (MEDIEVAL), and THIS WAY UP. Once again they could only grasp in outline what was happening. Once or twice they made out the words 'War' and 'Bombs' through the cosy wrapping material, but it was clear that even the bravest of them could do nothing helpful.

Piecing it together afterwards they understood that they had travelled with lots of other boxes a long distance from the Museum, and had gone underground until it was safe to return, very much later. At the time they felt curiously relaxed in this new environment, and many of them revived the practice of Hibernation, just as in the old days, while they had the opportunity. There was no doubt that normal Museum life, with its inevitable round of daily invasions by Visitors, was rather apt to disturb even the deepest sleeper.

CHAPTER 17

In Which Malingering is Shown to be Wrong

This hiccup in the lives of the chessmen came to its end, and after a lot of fuss and bother they found themselves being unwrapped yet again. They were welcomed back with smiles and laughter, and soon installed in newer and smarter quarters in a freshly-painted gallery. Before long the crowds were back too, and then it seemed as if they had never left the Museum at all.

Tiresome and intrusive photographers were now probably the most irritating aspect of their lives. Usually they brought out deeply unpleasant flashing devices that blinded the pieces for hours afterwards, and gave many of the Queens a headache. One or two, charged by the Museum with the production of Postcards, had a tendency to mouth 'Smile' or 'Say Cheese' at the Monarchy, which had some of the Warders biting their shields to prevent themselves from involuntary gestures or other forms of unworthy rudeness.

Occasionally their leisurely, untroubled life was interrupted by a sort of medical examination, when they were gently taken away to other hidden rooms blissfully safe from the public eye. Here Gentlemen in White Coats looked at them under Special Lights with rather impressive shiny equipment, asking them, respectfully, to put out their tongues and say 'Ah'. Occasionally these gentlemen would mutter concernedly, and write things down like Mr Madden had done. The chessmen always felt much better after one of these trips, and from time to time, when they felt that they hadn't had one for too long, some of the whiter-faced chessmen used to try and look specially ill, to attract attention.

A small group of the pieces accomplished this with greater success than they anticipated, and as a result one of the Doctors suggested that they spend a period of time in a Special Transparent Box in the Department, where a close eye could be kept on them. At the time these pieces felt rather pleased with themselves, but it turned out that they had to live in a Dark Cupboard away from all the other chessmen and their Public, and in time they rather regretted what they had done.

CHAPTER 18

In Which Visionary Ideas are Set in Motion

One day a Curator in Edinburgh went to have a chat as usual with his Lewis chessmen. He wasn't sure whether or not he should tell them. On the whole they were very well-behaved, and he really felt that they deserved a treat after all this time, but the question was should he keep it for a surprise until the last moment, or tell them now?

'We've had a request from London ...' he began. The chessmen looked up from whatever they were doing. 'Put it this way, how would you fancy a little trip ...?'

Both of the two Greater Queens went extremely pale. 'Yes,' he said gently, 'What would you say to going to London for three months to see the Others?'

CHAPTER 19

In Which Similar Ideas Follow On

'I'm not sure whether it will really happen,' another curator was explaining politely through the glass in London, 'but we've sent an Invitation to Edinburgh. What would you say if the Others were to come down from Scotland and stay with us for a few months? It's a long time since you were all together, and we've got a Special Case that would be just the job. The others are ready now to come out of the Dark Cupboard. That means you could all get together here in London for the first time in absolutely ages. Think what you've got to talk about now ...'

CHAPTER 20

In Which Serious Travel Arrangements are Made

In the Royal Museum of Scotland special shapes for cut-outs were drawn round each of the eleven men, and a special bed of a soft foamy material was found to make them a safe travelling bed. 'We're going by train, but I'm afraid you'll not be able to look out the win-dows,' said the Curator. The chessmen were all too excited to care about windows. 'It's 1993 now,' said the Curator. 'You were last together in 1831. That's ... er ... one hundred and sixty-two years ... isn't it?' There was silence from everybody while they thought this over. But he was right.

When they arrived in the British Museum the Lewis Chessmen would all be together again for the first time in 162 years.

CHAPTER 21

In Which Humans are Unnecessarily Slow

There was a great deal of hand-shaking and congratulation between the Curators. The Lewis Chessmen who lived in London were already set out in the New Showcase lined with New Velvet, and they watched anxiously as a promising-looking box was laid carefully on a table while the Curators continued to shake hands and congratulate one another. Then, exasperatingly, they closed a door on the box, and went off for lunch.

'... long journey ... cup of tea ... '

'... see what we can do about a sandwich ...'

'Good idea, before we get down to work ...'

The Chessmen waited, each side of the door, with their customary patience.

———◆———

Before they picked up any of the chessmen, the Curators put on White Gloves as a sign of respect. This touched the Queens and Kings, despite their agitation, because they couldn't help remembering some of the individuals who had manhandled them in the past. They re-called the sensation with distaste even after all that time.

Before much longer the lid was open, and one by one the familiar faces reappeared: two Kings, three Queens, three Bishops, one Knight and two Warders. One by one they were checked off on the list, and one by one they joined the others in the New Showcase. Everybody felt a bit shy while the curators were there, moving pieces about experimentally, and exclaiming with pleasure as they did so. Eventually things were felt to be ready, and once the Special Water Tray and the Special Meter had been put in, the case was safely shut and locked.

The curators lowered the lights and left the gallery. All eight Queens raised their drinking horns in a toast: 'Together again at last.' There was a noisy buzz of talk ...

CHAPTER 22

In Which the Lewis Chessmen Finally Receive their Due Accolade

The Lewis Chessmen were back in their correct positions by the time the doors swung back for the public. From their privileged position they could see that the cases around the walls contained other sorts of chess-pieces. When the exhibition was open, boys and girls charged round the cases, staring at the chessmen.

'I wonder which ones go with which ...?'

'Why are they all the same colour...?'

'Why are they all so serious ...?'

'I'd love to play with them, wouldn't you ...?'

One day a particularly interested visitor spent a long time inspecting them, walking round and round the case, his quick eyes taking in all details, and appraising the pieces individually. The rumour spread fast from an overheard remark. Someone had identified him: it was the *World Chess Champion* himself, dropped in to see them in time before the Edinburgh pieces went home for Christmas. The Bishops could hardly conceal their interest, the Warders stood to attention like ramrods, and even the Kings and Queens tried to catch his eye, and offer their service for a match over the board.

'If he's really that good,' thought a Knight to himself, 'why hasn't *he* got a crown?'

The End

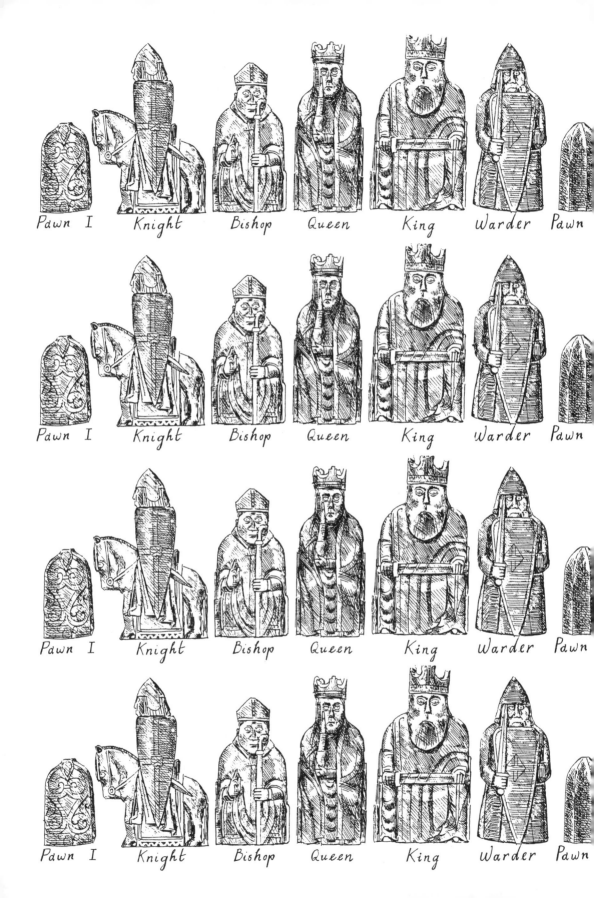

Pawn I   Knight   Bishop   Queen   King   Warder   Pawn

Pawn I   Knight   Bishop   Queen   King   Warder   Pawn

Pawn I   Knight   Bishop   Queen   King   Warder   Pawn

Pawn I   Knight   Bishop   Queen   King   Warder   Pawn